D0514733

Enchanting Ornamentation

COLOUR IN & RELAX

Set aside your mobile phone and switch off your computer to ensure peace and quiet while you colour in. Don't be distracted by any external stimuli or noises.

Concentrate completely on the lines and shapes in front of you, and on your pencil and hand movements. Put all thoughts to the back of your mind, immersing yourself instead in the world of your design. Become one with the patterns on your page and lose yourself in the shapes and colours.

You'll find yourself unwinding as you colour in, your mind clearing as you discover a completely new way to relax.

Colouring in these enchanting ornamentations will induce a feeling of peace and calm, as you create your own personal kaleidoscope of colour in the intricate images in this book.

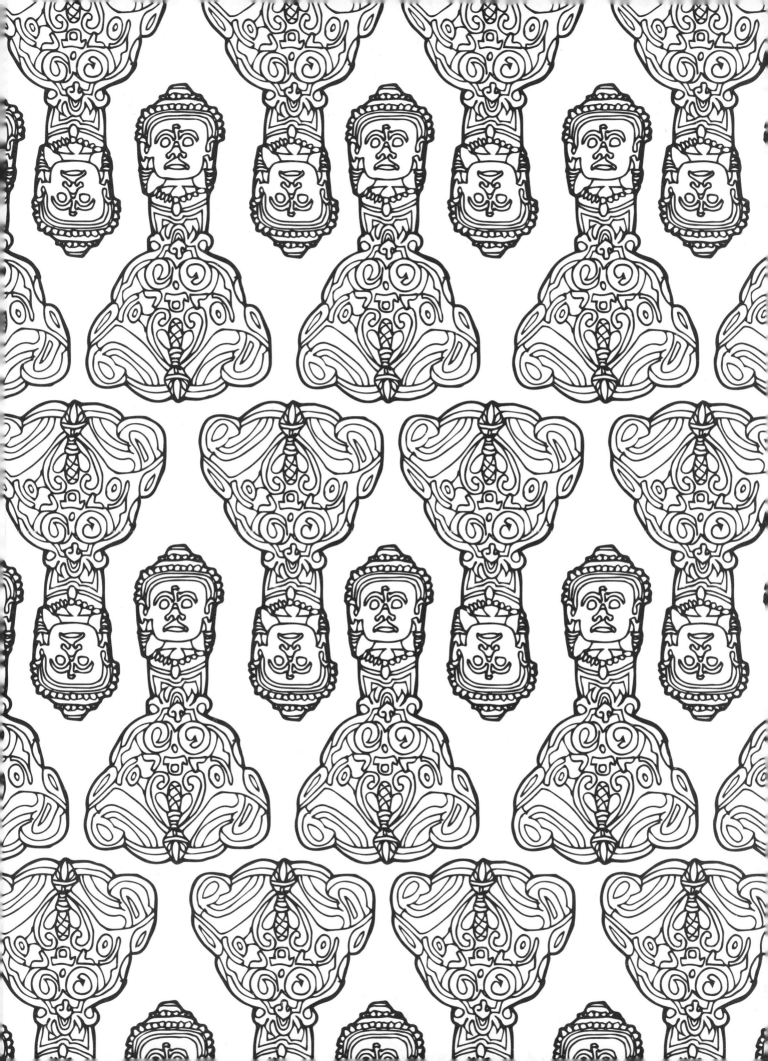

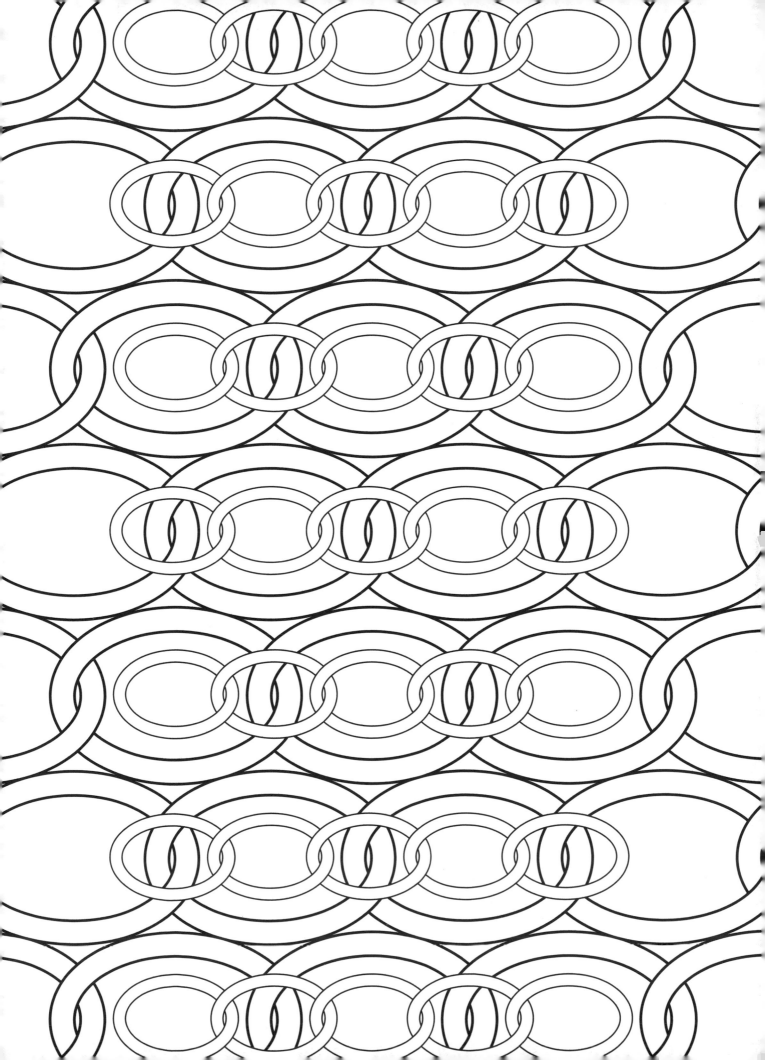

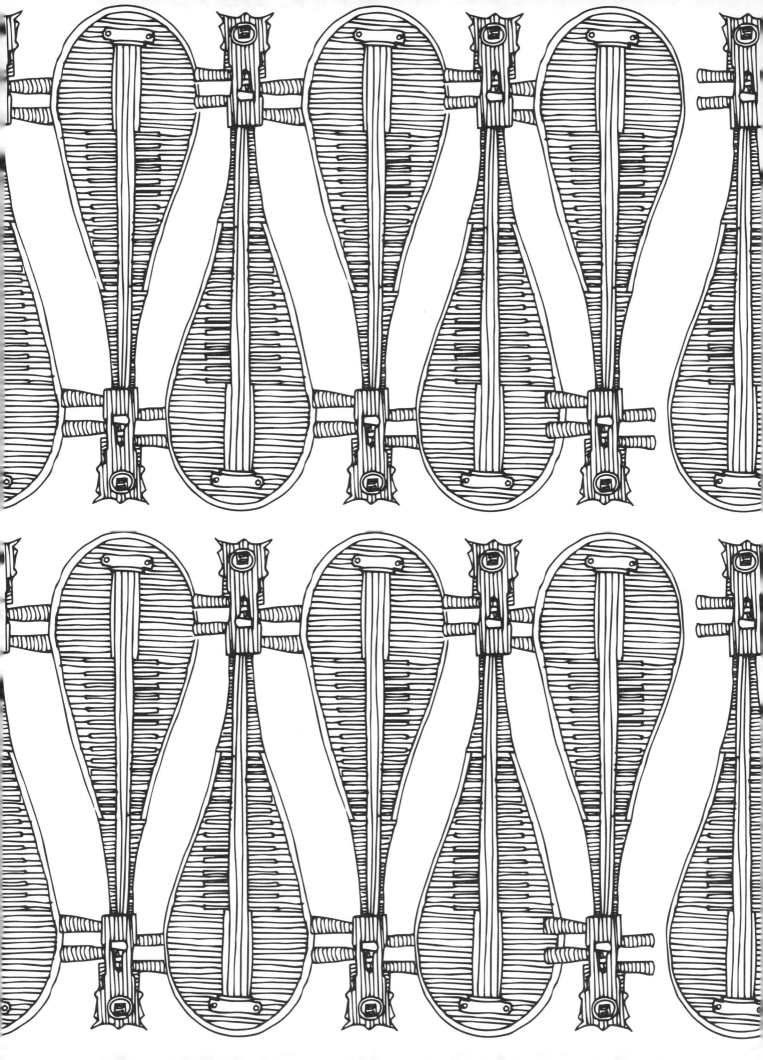

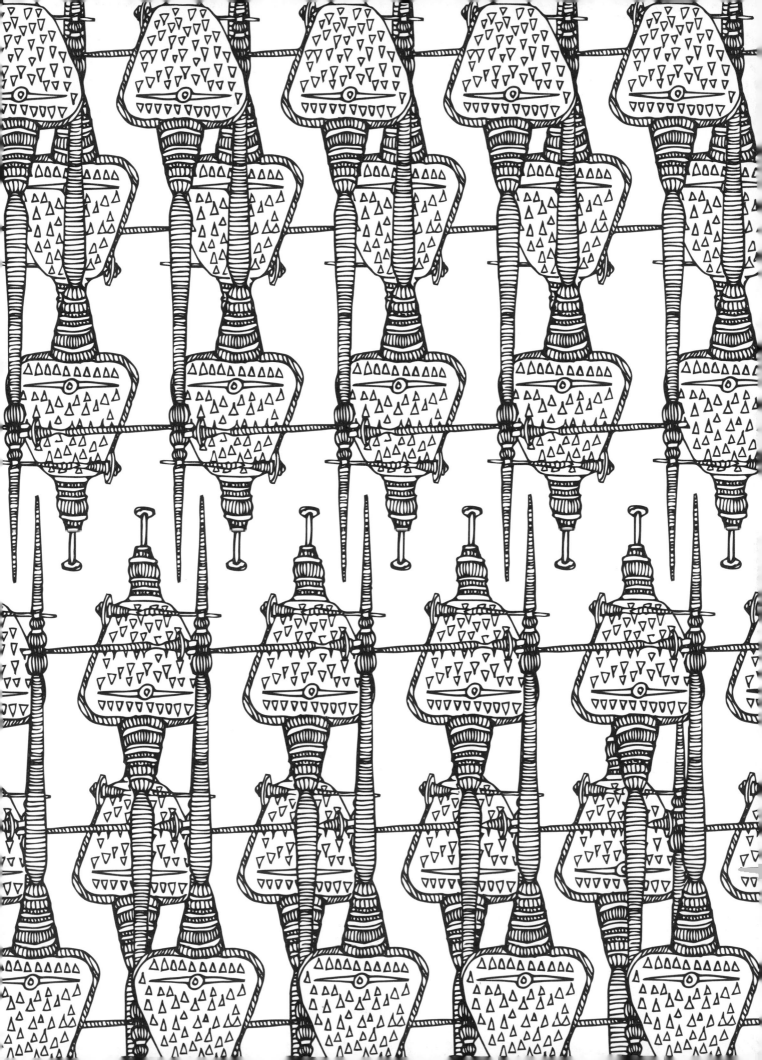

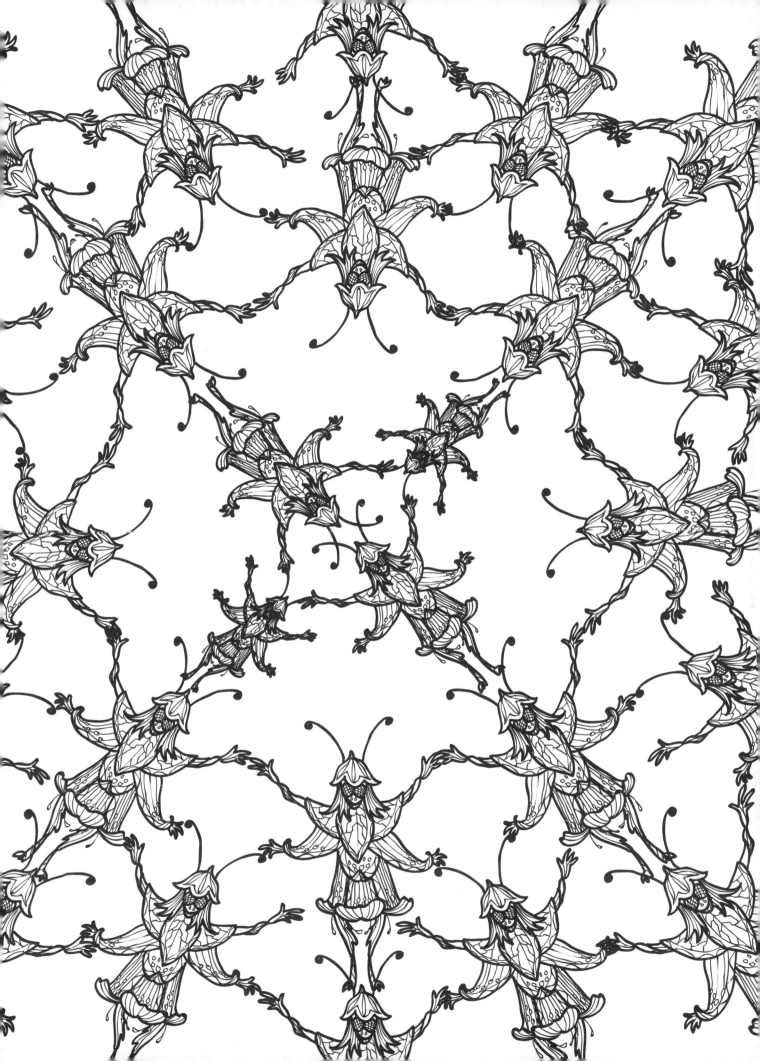